Drum Kit 3

Pieces & Exercises

for Trinity College London exams
2014–2019

Grades 5 & 6

Published by
Trinity College London

Registered Office:
89 Albert Embankment
London SE1 7TP UK

T +44 (0)20 7820 6100
F +44 (0)20 7820 6161
E music@trinitycollege.co.uk
www.trinitycollege.co.uk

Registered in the UK
Company no. 02683033
Charity no. 1014792

Music processed by Moira Roach.
Printed in England by Halstan, Amersham, Bucks.

Trinity College London graded drum kit examinations

Introduction

The aim of the Trinity College London drum kit syllabus is the development of versatile musicians, confident to play with authority, creativity and sensitivity across a broad range of styles and able to read and interpret drum charts with conviction and flair.

Drum kit examinations

Candidates are required to perform:

- two exercises. The first is chosen by the candidate, the other is chosen by the examiner from the remaining two exercises.
- two pieces from Group A (played with a backing track, with or without click, or live piano accompaniment)
- one piece from Group B (unaccompanied)
- two supporting tests

Exercises are specially written pieces that involve all the rudiments set for a particular grade (see cumulative rudiments grid). These rudiments are set out at the beginning of each grade section. Candidates will be required to learn these in order to be able to play the exercises.

Group A pieces have full backing accompaniment on CD, with and without click track, or piano accompaniment where appropriate. Candidates will be marked on their ability to interpret a typical drum chart and interact with the backing in terms of time-keeping, phrasing, soloing etc.

Group B pieces are unaccompanied.

Supporting Tests explore the candidate's perception and broader knowledge.

For full details on how to enter for an exam, venue equipment, supporting tests and how the exams are assessed, please refer to the current syllabus booklet which can be found at www.trinitycollege.co.uk

Drum kit rudiments

Rudiment	Grade 1	Grade 2	Grade 3	Grade 4	Grade 5	Grade 6	Grade 7	Grade 8
Single strokes	✓	✓	✓	✓	✓	✓	✓	✓
Double strokes	✓	✓	✓	✓	✓	✓	✓	✓
Single paradiddle	✓	✓	✓	✓	✓	✓	✓	✓
Flam		✓	✓	✓	✓	✓	✓	✓
Drag		✓	✓	✓	✓	✓	✓	✓
Four stroke ruff		✓	✓	✓	✓	✓	✓	✓
Five stroke roll			✓	✓	✓	✓	✓	✓
Seven stroke roll			✓	✓	✓	✓	✓	✓
Nine stroke roll			✓	✓	✓	✓	✓	✓
Flam tap				✓	✓	✓	✓	✓
Flam accent				✓	✓	✓	✓	✓
Flamacue				✓	✓	✓	✓	✓
Flam paradiddle				✓	✓	✓	✓	✓
Double paradiddle				✓	✓	✓	✓	✓
Paradiddle-diddle				✓	✓	✓	✓	✓
Drag and stroke					✓	✓	✓	✓
Double drag and stroke					✓	✓	✓	✓
Drag paradiddle					✓	✓	✓	✓
Single ratamacue					✓	✓	✓	✓
Double ratamacue					✓	✓	✓	✓
Triple ratamacue					✓	✓	✓	✓
Triple paradiddle						✓	✓	✓
Reverse paradiddle						✓	✓	✓
Pata fla fla							✓	✓
Swiss army triplet							✓	✓
Inward paradiddle							✓	✓

Drum kit notation key

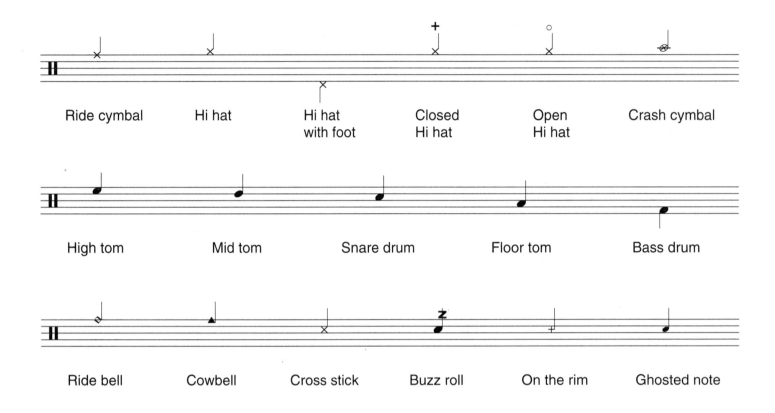

Please note that the notation used for ride cymbal (and bell), crash cymbal and cross stick has changed from that used in previous Trinity College London exam publications. Drum kit notation varies between different publishers/arrangers but the key above is becoming more consistently used.

Performance notes

General note for both grades

Where a crash cymbal appears at the start of a bar and is followed by one-bar repeat signs (|———𝄎———|), the crash cymbal should **not** be played in the repeat bars. If a crash cymbal is required it will be notated above the repeated bar in question. This is universally accepted as standard drum kit notation and it is the aim of the Trinity College London syllabus to encourage students to become familiar with what they will be confronted with in the real world of drum kit performance.

All repeats, including those within *da capo* and *dal segno* sections, should be observed in drum kit examinations (unless otherwise stated).

Candidates may use the backing track with or without clicks in the examination.

Grade 5

Neil Robinson   Exercise no. 1

This exercise is based on a shuffle feel which lends itself to the use of the drag and stroke and double drag and stroke rudiments. The paradiddle in bar 8 should have a straight 16s feel.

Use flam taps between ride and snare in bars 9 and 13 and be careful with the flam taps in bar 10 which have a straight 8s feel as does the flamacue in bar 12.

Neil Robinson   Exercise no. 2

Be careful not to push on during this exercise as it will make the demisemiquavers/thirty-second notes in bars 8 and 10, which should be played using paradiddles, tricky to play.

The opening section should have a solid semiquaver/sixteenth note groove with a drum and bass feel for the middle section.

Neil Robinson   Exercise no. 3

This exercise starts with double paradiddles then uses paradiddle-diddles (for a jazz feel) alternating with various rudiments as fill bars. There's a challenging single, double and triple ratamacue section from bar 12 moving into a solid straight 8s feel for the flam paradiddle section building to the end.

Malcolm Ball   Lime Tree Bay

This big-band composition begins with brushes and changes to sticks. The 'open' chart means interpretation is up to the player so interaction and creativity is key. Study the catalogues of Count Basie and Woody Herman for stylistic guidance.

Dave Frishberg
arr. George Double   You Would Rather Have the Blues

This arrangement places the Dave Frishberg wry original in a New Orleans, 2nd-line setting. For a convincing feel, there must be a clear contrast between the accents and ghosted notes on the snare drum, and the rolls should be played in tempo, as buzzed or bounced quavers/eighth notes. Listen to and research the recent work of drummer Stanton Moore for stylistic insight. The figures above the stave from bar 32 should be subtly realised and serve to support the rhythm of the piano part.

Troy Miller   Yabba Dabba

Aim to maintain a consistent and even sound to keep the feel 'in the pocket'. Be aware of the relationship between snare/bass drum and cymbals (cymbals can be slightly lower than the drums in dynamic). Also watch out for the unison notes and make them cohesive and tight.

Make the solo section (bar 21 onwards) in keeping with the style i.e. The Meters, Don Blackman, Bernard Wright, Tom Browne etc.

Andrew Tween/
Jonathan Taylor — On the Path

The piece takes influence from the recordings of contemporary European Jazz label 'ECM'. Famous kit players that have played for this label include Jon Christenson, Peter Erskine and Paul Motion.

In the opening snare figure, control is needed between the accents and non accents. Different stickings can be explored to help realise the contrast in articulation.

Open and closed rolls give different colours to the main $\frac{5}{4}$ groove pattern built around the snare.

George Double — Benton Street Bop

This is an energetic, dance-like piece which relies on strict observation of pulse and tempo and on broadly contrasted dynamics to create tension and excitement.

The first section is a Boogaloo, and should have a sense of moving forward, without rushing. Ensure there is contrast between ghosted and non-ghosted snare notes. From bar 15 there are single stroke semiquaver/sixteenth note ideas around the drums. Strive for a consistent and balanced sound between hands here. Throughout the piece buzz rolls have been written out as quaver/eighth note triplets; blend one buzzed stroke smoothly into the next to create an uninterrupted, continuous roll.

Paul Francis — Samba Time

The piece starts with a five stroke roll. A buzz roll appears at bar 9 and again at bar 17. Also, look out for an extra bass drum beat that is added in bars 9-12.

There are various accented beats throughout the piece. Try to play the non-accented snare beats with a softer approach allowing the tom beats to stand out more; this will create a better samba carnival feel.

Grade 6

Neil Robinson — Exercise no. 1

This exercise uses a 16s feel, paradiddle-based groove with an emphasis on control of the open hi hat in the main groove and doubles within the fill bars. Be careful not to be too heavy with the non-accented snare notes.

Neil Robinson — Exercise no. 2

For this exercise a triple paradiddle is used to create an Afro-beat feel in the first section with reverse paradiddle being used in the second section. The accents are important to help create the right feel. The flam accents in bars 1 and 5 should be played with a straight 16s feel.

Neil Robinson — Exercise no. 3

This exercise should have an Afro-Cuban feel for the main groove using double paradiddles switching between straight 8s and triplet feel for the fills. There is a $\frac{3}{4}$ section using flam taps and flam accents at bar 10 before returning back to the Afro-Cuban feel for the closing section.

George Double/
Adam Double — Warning

This song is broadly in the style of guitarist/singer John Mayer and has a contemporary blues-rock feel.

The opening groove requires strict control and independence of right hand on the floor tom and right foot on the bass drum. Keep the shuffled semiquaver/sixteenth note subdivision running in your head to maintain the right feel throughout. To begin with, practise different combinations of strokes between hands and feet with a metronome at slower tempos to build confidence.

The chorus groove should be big and fully projected, but ensure the backing track remains clearly audible at all times. The groove patterns follow the rhythm of the ensemble, try to phrase sympathetically with the band to make the playing sit with the track.

Dave Holland/
Matt McDonough   London Town

A funk/latin piece which utilises a straight 16th beat, along with a songo style latin chorus section.

The songo style of drumming is more of a concept than one particular 'beat'. Songo is a blend of folkloric and contemporary Cuban styles with elements of funk and jazz. In many ways, songo is the 'jazz' of Cuban drumming. The Cuban drummer Changuito was an early developer of the songo idea.

To prepare the songo pattern in the chorus, separate the hands and feet to learn the parts, then put them together. Note the left hand uses a circular movement around the snare, hi hat and tom.

The verse groove relies on a tight, funky feel. Ensure the hi hats are firmly closed to achieve the right stylistic sound.

The drum fills at the end of the piece are written 'ad lib'. In essence, you are free to play what you like here, but make sure it fits with the energy and direction the piece is moving towards as it nears the end.

Troy Miller   Aiden's Song

Keep the touch light throughout this piece and think in long phrases as opposed to individual bars i.e. linear; this will become easier with familiarity. Try also to lock in with the percussion and not fight it. Remember when using a backing track that it doesn't play to you, you have to play to it. Let the cymbal section from bar 13 breathe to make a contrast from the rest of the piece. References: Wayne Shorter, Weather Report and Brecker Brothers.

Andrew Tween/
Jonathan Taylor   Funky March

Much of this piece calls for control in dynamics between the right and left hand. In the A section most of the accents are taken by the right hand with ghost notes taken by the left. For this piece to work, the difference in dynamics is important.

From letter C the approach changes with more of an even dynamic between hands with occasional accents on the left hand on the hi hat such as at bars 12 and 16.

Accents coincide with punctuations from the band. A good sense of inner pulse is needed for the groove and stabs (accents with the band) to sit properly.

Matt McDonough   Funkylicious

This piece focuses on groove, ghosting and a predominantly off-beat hi hat, over which the rest of the kit is layered. The feel should be driving throughout, avoiding any temptation to drag.

Concentrate on the accuracy of each note to ensure that the individual parts work successfully together. Note, for example, the hi hat demisemiquavers/thirty-second notes in bars 6 and 8 – these should be practised until the whole bar is even in rhythmic placement and volume.

The snares are turned off in the middle section, which is an opportunity to enjoy the contrast between non-accented and accented notes on the snare. Make sure this is still played with a nice, groovy off-beat feel from the hi hat.

As we come to the next section, it is important that the left hand ghost notes are truly played with a light touch, helping to thicken up the groove, yet remaining distinctly different in volume.

Ralph Salmins   V is for Vernel

This piece for brushes is inspired by the great New Orleans drummer Vernel Fournier. Fournier was famous for his swinging and sensitive brush playing in the Ahmad Jamal Trio, apparently one of Miles Davis' favourite bands. Ahmad's version of *Poinciana* is legendary, as is Vernel's unusual groove on the tune. For some stylistic inspiration, listen to Ahmad's version of *Billy Boy* from Cross Country Tour 1958–1961.

This is a medium up-tempo piece incorporating some straight time, swishing and a melodic theme. There is also use of Be-bop language, combining hands and feet in the same phrase. Accented notes should be clearly brought out and played with energy and excitement.

Grade 5 Rudiments

You will need to learn the rudiments up to Grade 4 and the following to be able to play the Grade 5 Exercises.

Drag and stroke

Double drag and stroke

Drag paradiddle

Single ratamacue

Double ratamacue

Triple ratamacue

If you are left handed you may reverse the sticking.

Candidates must prepare all three exercises, but only two will be played during the exam. One is chosen by the candidate, the other by the examiner. (If you are left handed you may reverse the sticking.)

Grade 5 Exercises
Exercise no. 1

Neil Robinson

Remember to look at the Performance Notes on pages 5-7

Exercise no. 2

Neil Robinson

Remember to look at the Performance Notes on pages 5-7

Exercise no. 3

Neil Robinson

Remember to look at the Performance Notes on pages 5-7

Track 4 – Demo
Track 5 – With click
Track 6 – Without click

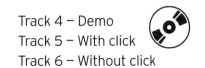

Lime Tree Bay

Malcolm Ball

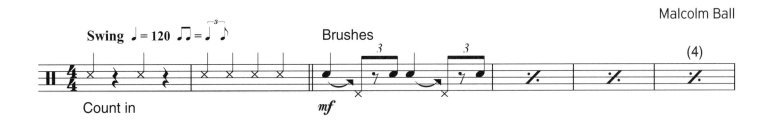

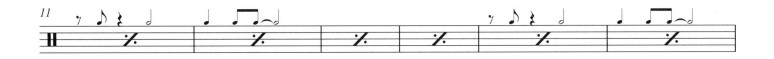

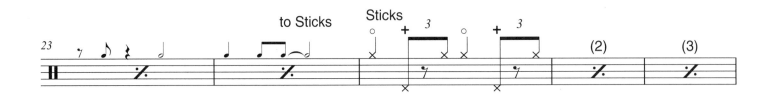

= stir or swish brush.

Ride 4 / Comp and fill as required

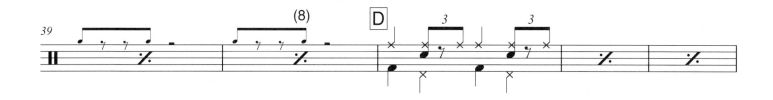

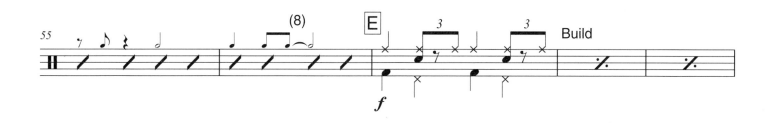

Remember to look at the Performance Notes on pages 5-7

Track 7 – Demo
Track 8 – With click
Track 9 – Without click

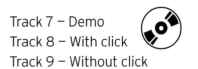

You Would Rather Have the Blues

Dave Frishberg
arr. George Double

Published by Bucks Music Group Limited on behalf of Bicycle Music Company.

('You could
get a break')

('You would
rather have
the blues')

Swing 4-feel

Cont. sim. with subtle figures

Set up

Swing 4-feel

Choke   ('Apparently you
choose the blues')

SOLO Break

Sharp
choke

Remember to look at the Performance Notes on pages 5-7

Track 10 – Demo
Track 11 – With click
Track 12 – Without click

Yabba Dabba

Troy Miller

Remember to look at the Performance Notes on pages 5-7

Track 13 – Demo
Track 14 – With click
Track 15 – Without click

On the Path

Andrew Tween/Jonathan Taylor

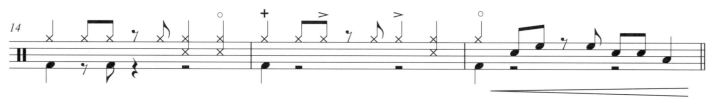

This piece can be performed in the exam with *either* the CD backing track,
or with a live accompanist using the supplied piano part.

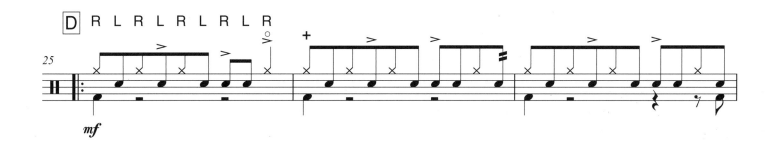

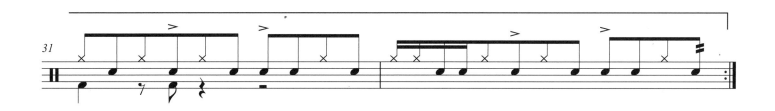

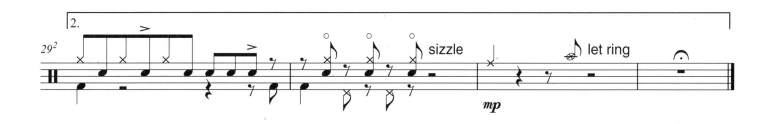

Remember to look at the Performance Notes on pages 5-7

Benton Street Bop

George Double

No repeat on the D.S.

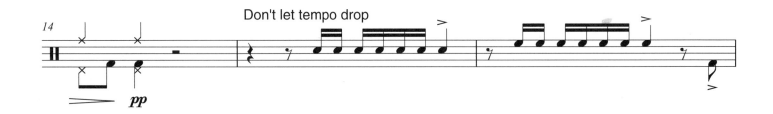

Don't let tempo drop

Drum Kit 3

Piano accompaniment

for Trinity College London exams 2014–2019

Grades 5 & 6

Published by
Trinity College London
Registered Office:
89 Albert Embankment
London SE1 7TP UK

T +44 (0)20 7820 6100
F +44 (0)20 7820 6161
E music@trinitycollege.co.uk
www.trinitycollege.co.uk

Registered in the UK
Company no. 02683033
Charity no. 1014792

Music processed by Moira Roach.
Piano part supplied by www.grooveworld.co.uk
Printed in England by Halstan, Amersham, Bucks.

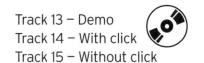

Track 13 – Demo
Track 14 – With click
Track 15 – Without click

On the Path

Andrew Tween/Jonathan Taylor

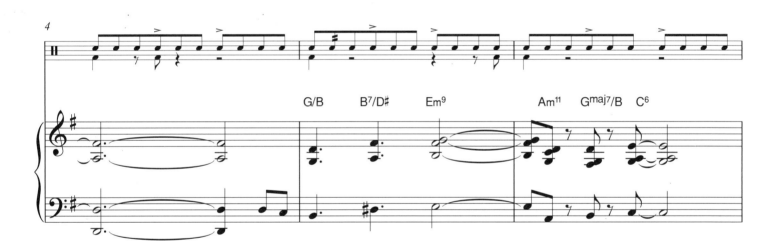

3

Track 30 – Demo
Track 31 – With click
Track 32 – Without click

Funky March

Andrew Tween/Jonathan Taylor

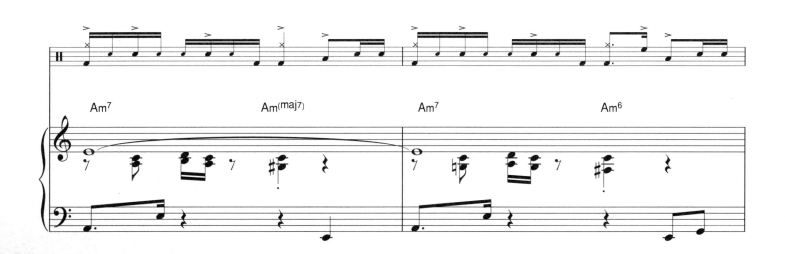

Piano part supplied by www.grooveworld.co.uk

Half time feel

mp

D.S. al Coda

mf

p

Coda

sfp — *f*   *p* — *f*   *p* — *f*   *pp*

Remember to look at the Performance Notes on pages 5-7

Samba Time

Paul Francis

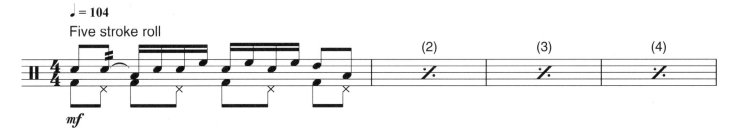

Grade 6 Rudiments

You will need to learn the rudiments up to Grade 5 and the following to be able to play the Grade 6 Exercises.

Triple paradiddle

Reverse paradiddle

If you are left handed you may reverse the sticking.

Candidates must prepare all three exercises, but only two will be played during the exam. One is chosen by the candidate, the other by the examiner. (If you are left handed you may reverse the sticking.)

Grade 6 Exercises
Exercise no. 1

Neil Robinson

Remember to look at the Performance Notes on pages 5-7

Exercise no. 2

Remember to look at the Performance Notes on pages 5-7

26

Exercise no. 3

Neil Robinson

Remember to look at the Performance Notes on pages 5-7

* No repeat on the D.S.

Track 21 – Demo
Track 22 – With click
Track 23 – Without click

Warning

George Double/Adam Double

Remember to look at the Performance Notes on pages 5-7

Track 24 – Demo
Track 25 – With click
Track 26 – Without click

London Town

Dave Holland/Matt McDonough

Tight Funk/Latin ♩ = 104

Count in

(Verse)
(Voice: 'Under ground in London Town')

Remember to look at the Performance Notes on pages 5-7

Track 27 – Demo
Track 28 – With click
Track 29 – Without click

Aiden's Song

Troy Miller

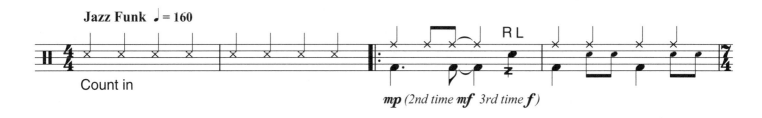

Track 30 – Demo
Track 31 – With click
Track 32 – Without click

Funky March

Andrew Tween/Jonathan Taylor

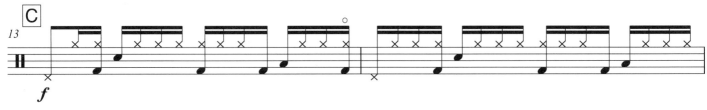

This piece can be performed in the exam with *either* the CD backing track,
or with a live accompanist using the supplied piano part.

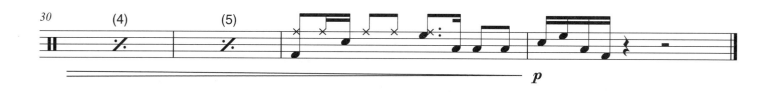

Remember to look at the Performance Notes on pages 5-7

Funkylicious

Matt McDonough.

Remember to look at the Performance Notes on pages 5-7

V is for Vernel

Ralph Salmins

Swish

sub. **p** *cresc. poco a poco*

Splash hats with foot

CD track listing

Grade 5

1.	Exercise no. 1	Robinson	0'48"
2.	Exercise no. 2	Robinson	0'48"
3.	Exercise no. 3	Robinson	0'41"
4.	Lime Tree Bay	Ball	2'18"
5.	Lime Tree Bay (backing track with click)	Ball	2'22"
6.	Lime Tree Bay (backing track without click)	Ball	2'22"
7.	You Would Rather Have the Blues	Frishberg *arr.* Double	1'38"
8.	You Would Rather Have the Blues (backing track with click)	Frishberg *arr.* Double	1'41"
9.	You Would Rather Have the Blues (backing track without click)	Frishberg *arr.* Double	1'41"
10.	Yabba Dabba	Miller	2'09"
11.	Yabba Dabba (backing track with click)	Miller	2'15"
12.	Yabba Dabba (backing track without click)	Miller	2'15"
13.	On the Path	Tween/Taylor	1'47"
14.	On the Path (backing track with click)	Tween/Taylor	1'48"
15.	On the Path (backing track without click)	Tween/Taylor	1'48"
16.	Benton Street Bop	Double	1'08"
17.	Samba Time	Francis	1'29"

Grade 6

18.	Exercise no. 1	Robinson	0'53"
19.	Exercise no. 2	Robinson	0'53"
20.	Exercise no. 3	Robinson	0'54"
21.	Warning	Double/Double	2'23"
22.	Warning (backing track with click)	Double/Double	2'29"
23.	Warning (backing track without click)	Double/Double	2'29"
24.	London Town	Holland/McDonough	2'14"
25.	London Town (backing track with click)	Holland/McDonough	2'16"
26.	London Town (backing track without click)	Holland/McDonough	2'16"
27.	Aiden's Song	Miller	2'29"
28.	Aiden's Song (backing track with click)	Miller	2'31"
29.	Aiden's Song (backing track without click)	Miller	2'32"
30.	Funky March	Tween/Taylor	1'51"
31.	Funky March (backing track with click)	Tween/Taylor	1'53"
32.	Funky March (backing track without click)	Tween/Taylor	1'53"
33.	Funkylicious	McDonough	1'36"
34.	V is for Vernel	Salmins	0'52"